Dear Reader,

The book you are holding came about in a rather different way to most others. It was funded directly by readers through a new website: Unbound. Unbound is the creation of three writers. We started the company because we believed there had to be a better deal for both writers and readers. On the Unbound website, authors share the ideas for the books they want to write directly with readers. If enough of you support the book by pledging for it in advance, we produce a beautifully bound special subscribers' edition and distribute a regular edition and ebook wherever books are sold, in shops and online.

This new way of publishing is actually a very old idea (Samuel Johnson funded his dictionary this way). We're just using the internet to build each writer a network of patrons. At the back of this book, you'll find the names of all the people who made it happen.

Publishing in this way means readers are no longer just passive consumers of the books they buy, and authors are free to write the books they really want. They get a much fairer return too – half the profits their books generate, rather than a tiny percentage of the cover price.

If you're not yet a subscriber, we hope that you'll want to join our publishing revolution and have your name listed in one of our books in the future. To get you started, here is a £5 discount on your first pledge. Just visit unbound.com, make your pledge and type monster5 in the promo code box when you check out.

Thank you for your support,

Dan, Justin and John
Founders, Unbound

Unbound
6th Floor Mutual House, 70 Conduit Street, London W1S 2GF
www.unbound.com

A CIP record for this book is available from the British Library

ISBN 978-1-78352-624-6 (trade pbk)
ISBN 978-1-78352-626-0 (ebook)
ISBN 978-1-78352-625-3 (limited edition)

Printed in **Slovenia**

2 3 4 5 6 7 8 9

For Emilia, Mosi, Dénes and Jonah

written by

SEAN LEAHY

illustrated by

MIHALY ORODAN

In every town, there is one shop
that always changes its face.

In Stapleton, it was the
very last shop in town.

This particular shop had seen it all...

a bookshop,

a baker's,

even one of those shops that sells
everything and nothing at all.

OPENING
THE MONSTER
DELICIOUS TREATS FOR HUMANS

But one day, in the first drips of spring, a new sign appeared
in the window that caught the eye of everyone in town.

The chitter-chatter started soon after, with folk young and old wondering who these monsters were and where they had come from.

'No one asked me!' said Mr Broomstick, the newsagent at the other end of town.

'How peculiar,' mused Madame Le Bonque, the local hotelier.

But to Bib, it was the most wonderful
sign ever popped anywhere.

'Absolutely not,' Bib's mum sang
from the top of the stairs.

'Eat monsters' grub?' snorted Dad, with a mouth full of brown cereal.
'It'll be all gooey and weird. And besides, monsters eat people.'

But Bib's birthday was soon approaching. So one particularly sunny day, Bib pointed his mum, his dad, his nana and his baby sister, Isla, in the direction of the café.

Little was given away outside. Just a small name written
in chalk and the faintest whiff of deliciousness.

But quite the opposite was true behind the doors...

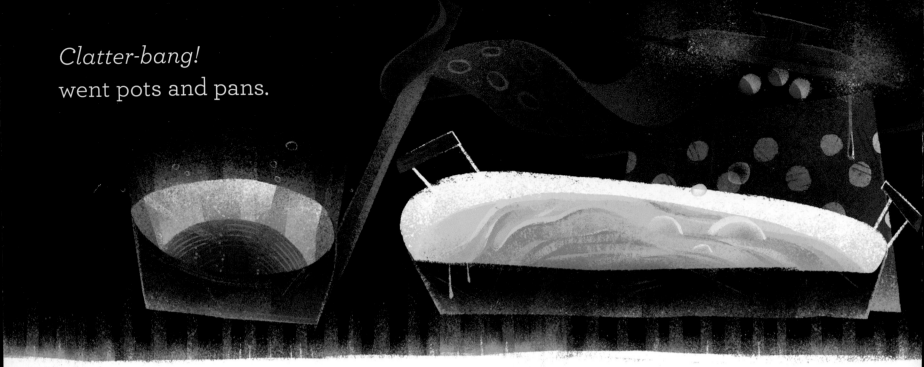

Clatter-bang!
went pots and pans.

Hubble-bubble!
sizzled stews and soups.

Honk and snort!
wagged chins and jaws.

'Table for four and a half, is it?' came a voice from nowhere.

'Um, yes please,' said Dad.

FAVOURITE CUSTOMERS
Luca Strawson   Desmond Farrell
Oliver Satterfield   Luke Grindal

A tiny creature, no bigger than a football (and just as plump), sprang out and gestured. 'Right this way.'

'I don't know what anything is,'
worried Mum. But Bib was too
busy watching the carry-on
to care.

'What can I get you?' asked the waitress,
locked eye to eye with Isla.

'Um, we'll order for the kids,' said Dad.

Dad ordered the safest-looking dishes on the menu, and the waitress slithered off to the kitchen.

'I'm just going to the loo,' said Mum.
'I feel rather queasy.'

And off she
hurriedly went.

Soon after, the waitress reappeared.
'Mummygatawny soup?'

'That's mine,' said Nana.

Dad gulped.
'I... I'd best go check on your mother.'
And off he went.

'Father beans?'
hissed the waitress.

'Those are for Mum,' said Nana.
'Where has she got to?'

'I'd best go take a look.
Watch your sister, Bib.'
And into the steam she disappeared.

'Who's having the 'nana split?'
Now Bib was nervous too.
'It's for my little sister,' he said.

The waitress placed the dish in
front of Isla and ruffled her hair.
'Bon appétit!'

'I'm worried about the grown-ups,' Bib told Isla.
'Twit will keep you safe,' he said, popping him
gently on her head.

'I'll go get them.'

He made his way
between tables, legs
and tails until he came
upon the kitchen door.

A quick peek
wouldn't hurt.

And as the door
squeaked open,
Bib could not
believe his eyes...

'Bring them over here,' growled the chef.
'They'll make a delicious pie.'

Bib was about to let out the
most enormous yell, but then
he saw his mum and dad peeling
and chopping and having a ball.

'What are you doing?'
he finally mumbled.

'Well, cooking of course!
This place is amazing!
You were right all along.'

'But where
is Nana?'
Bib asked.

Nana burst through
the doors...

'LASAGNA, TABLE TWELVE!'
she beamed.

'AND MAKE IT AN
EXTRA SLOPPY ONE!'

Bib was glad they saw what he knew all along. That the monsters
were friendly after all. And they *definitely* didn't eat people.

'Bib...' Mum worried.
'Where is Isla?'

'BABY FOOD, TABLE ONE!'

'Oh.'

Supporters

Unbound is a new kind of publishing house. Our books are funded directly by readers. This was a very popular idea during the late eighteenth and early nineteenth centuries. Now we have revived it for the internet age. It allows authors to write the books they really want to write and readers to support the books they would most like to see published.

The names listed below are of readers who have pledged their support and made this book happen. If you'd like to join them, visit www.unbound.com.

Hilary Alcock

Rosalind Alice

Moose Allain

Sophia Allen

Rev. N J Armitage-Hurrell

Laura and Jon Ashworth

Hannah Asprey

Neil Atkinson

Al Bailey

Maximum Bailey

Kora Katz Baker

David Ballard

Ágnes Bárkai

Keyan and Lyla Barnham

Olivia Barter

Melanie Bartheidel

Lee Batchelor

Chris Bell

Sandra Bird

Joe Birkin

Thomas Birts

Owen Bjarnason

Rebecca Blake

Miller & Neva Bowie

Keir Bradley

Neil Brand

Vanessa Bray

Siobhan Breach

Elly Brewer

Isla Brodie

Greg Browne

D Bubulj

Lucy Burton

Sandra Bushell

Jake, Amelie and Beau Butler

Dan Buxton

Ruby Callaghan

Anjee Campbell

Enid Campbell

Henry Carden

Jan Carr

Martine Carter

Anne Caulfield

Jack Caulfield

Zoe Caulfield

Rob Cavanagh

Adrian Cecil

Rohan Chadwick

Licia Chefai et Cédric Layrac

Andy Clarke

Peter Clary

Brittany Clayton

Jeremy Climas

Dara and Cillian Connell Lynott

Wendy Constance

Denise Cooper

Amber Costley

Skylar Crom

Michael Cunningham

J-F Cuvillier

Reuben D'Herville

Sarah Dalli-Jaques

Cloak Dangerfield

Wendy Davis

Scarlett Day Alexander

Kieran Delaney

Kate Denman

Gary Diamond

Sarah Dodds

Miche Doherty

Daphne Doody-Green

Patrick, Orla & Eloise
Dooney

John Douglas

Zoltán Dragon

Rachel Drayson

Chris Duncan

Sandra Duric

Atlas Eden

Oscar Edge

Mark Edwards

Gary Ekins

Jonathan Elliman

Peter Elliott

Helen Ellis

Rebecca Eudora

Amelia Evans

Shawn Patrick Farrell

Lynden Fiallos

Heather Forland

Jonny Francis

Peter Fraser

Great Aunt Jane Freshwater

Jon Gerlis

Ghost Mom

Claire Grantham

Scott Greatorex

Alex Green

Jane Green

Luke Grindal

Dan Grubb

Nara Alice Hallam

Janice Halsey

Dawn Hamilton

Gwilym Hardy

Bex Harman

Faye Hartley

Gabriel Thomas Vidal
Hayden

Amy Heath

Lucie Heath

Csaba Hegedűs

Mike Hemsley

Atlas Hewett & Everest
Hewett

Sarah Hibner

Scott Hoad

Jeff Horne

Dave House

Kristin Hronek

Daniel Humphreys

Emily Anne Hutchinson

Robert Iveson

Joseph and Adam Jackson

Susan Jackson

Freya James

Gill James

Rae Jana Kyle

Török Fruzsina Jázmin

Uncle Jez

Aliy Jones

Harendra Kapur

Jen Kavanagh

Emily Kearns

Charlie Keating

Skye Kelly-Barrett

Doug Kessler

Adam Ketterer

Arthur and Ernie Kiely

Chris Kiely

Dan Kieran

Elliot Kinsella

Jakub Korab

Isabelle Lawrence

David Leach

Laurie Leahy

Ryan Leahy

Niall Ledger

Bridget Caron Lee

Gary Lee

Naomi Lepora

James Lester

Cecelia Lewis

Elizabeth Lloyd-Hitt

Erin and Liam Louiset-Hall

Elizabeth Luckey

Eleanor Luker

Stuart Luker

Sarah MacTurtle

Noah and Jude Mafi-Wynn

Aidan Mahoney

Poppy & Isabella Major

Max Malek

Thomas & Ellie Mallon

Amanda Mancino-Williams

Alistair Martin

George Martin

MatCro

Matt Mawdsley

Kate Maxwell

Sophie McArdle

Nicola McArthur

Mark McCoy

Nathan McKeown

Joe McLaren

Andrew McMillan

Steven Melvin

Arthur & Sylvie Millhouse

Rory Milton

John Mitchinson

Oscar Anand Mittal

Stephen Molloy

Sonny Moore

Christine Morse

Kate Mounce

Kaydence Maggie Munns

Laura Murphy

Simon Murray

Alice & Holly Murrell

Tom Murtagh

Joe Murton

Carlo Navato

John New

Del Noble

Dulcie Noble

Matthew Nunn

Daniel O'Brien

Damien Owens

Nóra Papp

Thomas Parker

Deborah Partington

Oliver Paterson & Janek
    Lukowski

Graham Patrick

Mark Pavey

Charlie Patrick Pearson

Stuart Pearson

Tom Pennington

Callum Philp

Jack & Leila Phoenix

Justin Pollard

Robert Pooke

Keet Potato

Regan Rawlins

Sian Rees-Jones

Agustin M. Rejon

Franklin Retallick

Phil Revell

Debi Richardson

Alexandra Rodriguez

Montague Philip Leonidas
    Rogers

Rebecca Rose

Nicky Russell

Zoe Sadler

Viktor Sághy

Matthew Saunders

Emma and Aaron Schmidt

She She

Sean Sheehy

Lucie Shelton-Smith

Dan Simpson

Dan Smith

Dave Smith

Duncan Smith

Jennie Smith

Sharon Snow

K Squires

Ben Standage

Lorraine Stanhope

Owen & Millie Stokes

Cameron Stoneman

Michael Strawson

Glenn Sturgess

Jake Sturzaker

Erick Sumner

Graham Surrey

Arthur and Sam
    Sutherland-Kain

Nancy and Ruby Swanton

Natasha Szczerb

Laura Taflinger

Alexis Taylor

Trevor Thurlow

TJ, Ro

Daniel Toop

Jessica Tottman

Mr Townsend

Jessie Tracy

Irene Triendl

Arthur Tucker

Mollie & Georgia Udall

Jon Urie

Filippe Vasconcellos

Jamie Vidal

Michael Vincent

June W

Nancy Walbank

Lucy Jane Patricia Walker

Eliza Walsh

James Warbey

Vince Warne

Nina Waters

Paul Welander

Matilda Louise Eleanor West

Ralph Wettach

Phil Whisson

Chris White

Sophie Whitehouse

Carol Wickwire

Arnold Williams

Mark Willis

K Wise

Paul Withers

Matthew & Eleanor Worrall

Weiwei Xu

Yasmina & Uncle Mark

Dominic Young

Susan Zasikowski